THE "DENIZENS" WILL CONTINUE TO LIVE ON.

ACTING AS THEY PLEASE...

TWITCH

UNTIL THEIR FINAL MOMENTS.

SCSHH

AS LONG AS THEIR POWER ALLOWS...

...WERE THE HUMAN BEINGS THAT WISHED AND SWORE VENGEANCE AGAINST THE "DENIZENS," AND OBTAINED THE POWER OF UNUSUAL ABILITY BY DEVOTING THEIR ENTIRE EXISTENCES BEING THE CONTAINER OF THE "LORDS."

THE ONES WHO BECAME THE ADVANCE GUARDS OR THE WEAPONS OF THE "CRIMSON LORDS"...

"FLAME HAZE," THE DESTROYERS.

THOUGH TARGETED, CHASED, AND HUNTED BY THOSE DESTROYERS...

...THOSE WHO FEARED FOR THIS SITUATION BEGAN TO EMERGE.

IN TIME, AMONG THE "CRIMSON LORDS," THE "DENIZENS" OF GREAT POWER,...

IN THE FUTURE, THIS HUGE DISTORTION MAY CAUSE A TREMENDOUS CATASTROPHE IN BOTH THIS WORLD AND THE "CRIMSON WORLD"—

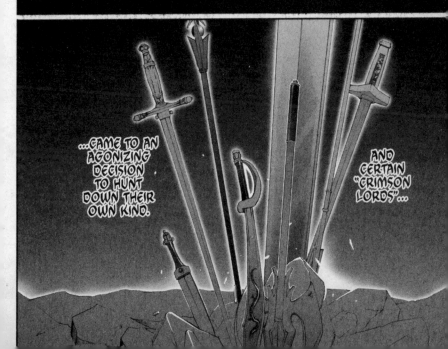

...CAME TO AN AGONIZING DECISION TO HUNT DOWN THEIR OWN KIND.

AND CERTAIN "CRIMSON LORDS"...

...THE DISTORTION EXPANDED AT AN ACCELERATED PACE.

THROUGH THIS CAREFREE RAMPAGE OF THE "CRIMSON DENIZENS," ...

THE HUMAN BEINGS, HAD THEIR "POWER OF EXISTENCE"...
AND BECAME NONEXISTENT.
THOSE MEANT TO EXTEND, CONNECT, AND SPREAD OUT...
...HAD THEIR EXISTENCE ELIMINATED,
CAUSING THE WORLD TO DISTORT—

THE "DENIZENS," WHO CROSSED OVER FROM THE "CRIMSON WORLD,"...

THEY ACT AS THEY PLEASE, AS LONG AS THEIR POWER ALLOWS, UNTIL THEIR FINAL MOMENTS.

WITH THAT POWER, THEY MANIFEST IN THIS WORLD AND FREELY CONTROL THE MYSTERIOUS PHENOMENA.

...ROBBED THE HUMAN BEINGS OF THE "POWER OF EXISTENCE," A FUNDAMENTAL ENERGY NEEDED TO EXIST IN THIS WORLD.

THE GENERAL NAME GIVEN TO THEM BY AN ANCIENT POET WAS...

...THE "CRIMSON DENIZENS."

THEIR WORLD IS NEXT DOOR TO THIS ONE, BUT IT CAN'T BE REACHED ON FOOT,

THEY CALLED IT THE "SWIRLING CATHEDRAL."

THE POET NAMED IT THE "CRIMSON WORLD."

FLOP

...PREVAIL IN THIS WORLD'S LIGHT AND DARKNESS.

THOSE NONHUMAN BEINGS...

~*Prologue*~

ORI BOOK STORE

BOOKS - STATIONERY

Shakugan no Shana

VOL 1

Story by Yashichiro Takahashi
Art by Ayato Sasakura

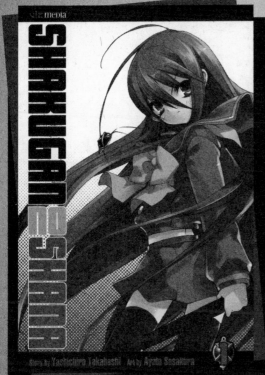

Saving the World Is Easier than Falling in Love

Yuji Sakai is beginning what he *thinks* will be the life of a normal high school student. But everything changes when the world around him stops, the surrounding people are engulfed in blue flames and a freakish doll-like creature begins sucking them up. Before Yuji suffers the same fate, a young redheaded girl with a sword appears and saves him. Yuji is drawn into the struggle between these creatures from another world, the Crimson Denizens, and the girl, Shana, a "Flame Haze." He too has a crucial role to play in the conflict, despite the fact that...he's dead!

- **$9.99**
- **Volume 1 available 4/17/07**
- ***Shakugan No Shana: The Girl with Fire in Her Eyes* novel available 4/17/07**

THE ENGLISH ROYAL FAMILY HAS A WELSH CORGI, TOO.

PANT
PANT

...WELL, THAT'S IT. GOT IT...?

THIS ONE IS A NO-TAIL PEMBROKE.

WELSH CORGI PEMBROKE

THIS DOG IS FAMOUS FOR BEING THE MODEL FOR "SNOOPY."

BEAGLE

...HEY. YOU OKAY...?

PAPILLON

WHEN THEY GROW UP, THEIR EARS LOOK LIKE BUTTERFLIES. SO IT'S NAMED PAPILLON, "BUTTERFLY" IN FRENCH.

GUU GUU

GA
GA

GUU GUU

FOOD

EMBARRASSED...

HMM... MR. MANAGER?

WHAT...?

IS... ISN'T THERE A DIFFERENT WAY TO ADDRESS ME?

SO INFORMAL?

UH, SURE, MR. MANAGER!!

ANYWAY, FIRST OF ALL, I NEED YOU TO CLEAN THE PUPPIES' BEDPANS.

HMM LET'S SEE...

THERE ARE 13 PUPPIES HERE. ALL OF THEM ARE IMPORTANT "MERCHANDISE."

I'LL DO MY BEST!

FIRST OF ALL, I'LL EXPLAIN THEIR TYPE, HOW OLD THEY ARE, FEATURES AND SO ON. LISTEN CAREFULLY AND MEMORIZE IT ASAP.

SURE THING!

YOU HAVE TO KNOW THEIR CONDITION AT ALL TIMES.

MERCHANDISE...

SORRY TO KEEP YOU WAITING.

OOOOW ...HERE COMES MY MASTER...

OH, YEAH... VERY NICE.

BUT SHE KNOWS HOW TO TAKE CARE OF DOGS BETTER THAN YOU.

NEVER HAD GIRL-STAFF, SO IT'S THE FIRST TIME I'M SEEING THIS BUT...

IS THIS STYLE, LIKE, WHAT YOU'RE INTO?

YOU IDIOT! IT'S THE SAME AS THE MAIN SHOP.

THIS SHOP IS THE SECOND SHOP...?

UHH, THIS IS MY ONLY STAFF, KENTARO.

HEY... NICE TO MEET YA...

MAN, THE DOGS' REACTION JUST NOW WAS PRETTY INSANE, EH?

MAYBE SHE'S A DOG TOO!

SHUT UP!!

YIPPEE.

WHOO-HOO! NEW STAFF!!

I DON'T HAVE TO CLEAN DOG CRAP ANY-MORE!

WOOFLES
わっふる

NO, WAY, SERIOUSLY ?!

THIS DOG IS THE ONE I TOLD YOU...

PANT

WHOSE DOG IS THIS?

YOU'RE HIRED AS A TEMP FOR NOW.

NEGISENBE...

YOU CAN DEAL WITH LOW PAY, RIGHT?

THA...

THANK YOU SO MUCH!

SEEMS TO HAVE... SOME- THING...

...THIS NAIVE "CRAZY FOR DOGS" GIRL...

...HOWEVER

I MUST HAVE BEEN BORN TO THIS FATE...

AH, CRAP... I PICKED UP ANOTHER STRAY DOG...

SIGH

WHY ARE YOU WEARING THAT COLLAR? YOU WORE IT LAST TIME TOO...

IT'S A BAD HABIT OF MINE. WHEN I FEEL SORRY FOR SOMETHING, I CAN'T JUST LEAVE IT....

I ALWAYS WEAR IT FOR GOOD LUCK.

THIS IS...LIKE THE ONE ON THE DOG THAT SAVED MY LIFE.

OH, WELL...

SHE'S NICE. YOU SHOULD HIRE HER.

I'M SURE SHE'LL WORK OUT!

PAP

HEY, MAN... THAT'S A LITTLE HARSH.

SHE CAME HERE...

I'M DONE FOR...

IF SHE SHOWS ME PUPPY EYES...

THIS IS THE SAME SITUA-TION.

I CAN'T LEAVE YOU...

NO, I CAN'T.

BOYHOOD TEPPEI

WHIMPER

WHIMPER

WHIMPER

AH. THIS IS MY HOME-TOWN SPECIALTY, NEGISEN-BEI* RICE. PLEASE ACCEPT IT!

I...I'M SORRY!

I...I DON'T WANT TO BE USELESS ANYMORE!! I JUST WANTED YOU TO HELP ME OUT...!!

I DON'T CARE. THAT WHOLE ATTITUDE OF DEPENDING ON OTHER PEOPLE IS WHY YOU'RE USELESS!!

IF YOU SAY SO, THANKS...

...NO THANKS. JUST GO HOME.

HMPH

* ONION RICE CRACKERS

I'LL MAKE UP FOR WHAT HAPPENED TO NOA. PLEASE LET ME WORK HERE!!

I PERSUADED MY PARENTS AND CAME ALL THE WAY HERE BY MYSELF.

PANT PANT PANT

YEAH...NOA WAS ATTACKED BY THIS MONGREL DOG AND IS NOW IN THE HOSPITAL FOR CHECKS...

I'M USELESS WITHOUT LUPIN.

...YOU'RE USELESS NO MATTER WHAT.

...WHY'D YOU BRING THIS DOG, TOO?!

AH... LUPIN IS...

PANT

I... I'M HERE.

...YOU'RE HERE...

WHO'S THIS? A FRIEND OF YOURS?

WHAAT-- OH, NOOO!!

A C K!

I NEVER SAID I'D HIRE YOU...

RIGHT AFTER THEY'RE BORN, THEIR MOTHER LICKS THEIR REAR ENDS TO HELP THEM PEE, AND THEY LIKE THE WAY THAT FEELS.

MILK MILK MILK

PUPPIES TEND TO PEE WHEN THEY'RE REALLY HAPPY. IT'S CALLED "HAPPY PEE."

MOMMA MOMMA

THAT CONNECTION STAYS, SO WHEN THEY'RE SO HAPPY THEY CAN'T STAND IT ANYMORE, THEY START TAKING A LEAK.

CHAPTER 2
I'LL DO MY BEST (FOR NOW)!

WOOF

RUF

RUF

RUF

HEY...WAIT A MINUTE. THEY WERE CALM BEFORE AND THEN SUDDENLY GOT ALL EXCITED...

YAP

YAP

AROOOO

WOW... AMAZ- ING...

WHAT'S UP WITH THEM?

YAAAP

Inubaka: Crazy for Dogs

VOL 1

By Yukiya Sakuragi

Country Dog, City Dog

All alone except for her loyal mutt Lupin, 18-year-old Suguri moves from the countryside to the big city to find a career and a new life! When she accepts a job at a pet store, she meets a variety of dogs and owners, each with thier own quirky personality. What she lacks in experience, she makes up for with her natural rapport with all things wagging and fluffy!

- $9.99
- Volume 1 available now

...TO HAVE A DREAM!!!

...

JIO'S GOING TO MAKE IT! HE'S GONNA MAKE IT!! HE'S GONNA MAKE IT!!! HE'S GONNA MAKE IT!!!

DAMN IT... THE VINES THEY'RE FIGHTING ON ARE BEGINNING TO BURN.

HSSSSH

BWOOOSH

WHY ARE YOU TAKING ORDERS FROM A BAD GUY LIKE SABAKI!?

I DON'T CARE WHO HIRES ME.

I JUST HATE GUYS WHO TALK ABOUT DREAMS AND HOPE.

FSH FSH

IT'S THE HATRED FOR THOSE WHO ARE ENJOYING LIFE IN COMFORT THAT MADE ME STRONG.

WHAT I GAINED FROM BEING ALONE AREN'T THINGS LIKE AFFECTION AND KINDNESS...

WORLD DOMINATION!!

THE THING THAT GAVE ME STRENGTH TO CARRY ON ALONE...

THAT WAS...

BM

KSH

GP

JIN, IT SEEMS LIKE I'M GOING TO HAVE FIGHT YOU AFTER ALL...

THE REASON IT'S BLACK IS BECAUSE OF THE SPIRIT RISING FROM MY BODY.

THE EFFECT OF MY O-PART IS AN ORDINARY FLAME.

NO.

SO THAT'S YOUR O-PART EFFECT, JIN?!

GGGGG

FSH FSH

STP

...FOR YOU, JIO...

MY SPIRIT IS FED BY MY HATRED...

...BUT THERE ARE CASES WHEN THE O.P.T.'S SPIRIT SLIGHTLY CHANGES THE NATURE OF THE O-PART EFFECT.

BASICALLY, THE O-PART EFFECT REMAINS THE SAME...

Sp

GGG

...ON THE VERY DAY I CALLED YOU MY FRIEND...

JIO...

THEY WERE KILLED, AND I KNOW THAT FOR A FACT. BECAUSE... I SAW IT WITH MY VERY EYES...

MY PARENTS DIDN'T DIE OF AN ACCIDENT.

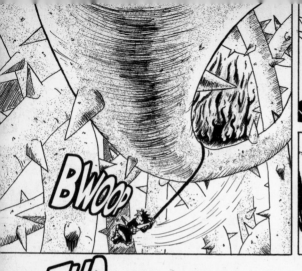

BWOOP

THD

I'M BACK... KICK!!!

URGH!!

...AND IT'LL NEVER GO OUT.

FSH

MY BLACK FLAME WILL KEEP ON BURNING UNTIL THE OBJECT IS REDUCED TO ASHES...

FSH

HA, THE TIP OF YOUR SCARF IS ON FIRE NOW.

GWOOO

BWOOOM

KOKUENCHU (BLACK FLAME PILLAR)

黒炎柱

WAAA!

PLL

PLL

HM.
SO HE
JUST
FELL BY
HIMSELF.

AAAAAH!

AAAARGH!

PLL

PLL

MR. LANG, ISN'T JIO HERE WITH YOU?

HUH?

THAT BLACK FLAME ISN'T JUST AN ORDINARY FIRE.

D... DAMN, THAT KID'S IN DANGER.

ONCE IT CAUGHT ON FIRE, THE FIRE DIDN'T DIE DOWN UNTIL IT BURNED EVERYTHING.

LOOK AT THAT BAG.

YEAH.

ARE YOU TELLING ME THAT JIO IS FIGHTING WITH AN O.P.T., RIGHT NOW?!

NO, JIO...

IF JIO TOUCHES THE BLACK FLAME EVEN ONCE, THAT'LL BE THE END OF HIM...

THAT'S RIGHT.

SO I HAVE NO CHOICE BUT TO FIGHT YOU...

RAA-AAA!!!

COME ON!!!

GGGG

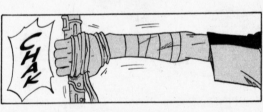

IF YOU DON'T FIGHT ME SERIOUSLY, YOU'RE NOT GONNA BE ABLE TO WIN, JIO.

WHY DON'T YOU INITIATE YOUR O-PART EFFECT?

SO, IS THAT YOUR O-PART?

BWaa

I'M GOING TO KILL YOU SLOWLY ONCE I'M DONE WITH HIM.

FASH

DON'T WORRY, OLD MAN.

FRRR

GSH

SO THAT'S WHAT A REAL O.P.T. IS LIKE...

I... I COULDN'T MOVE AT ALL...

IF YOU DON'T FIGHT ME, THEN THAT OLD MAN'S GONNA DIE FIRST.

SO, WHERE ARE YOU, JIO?

YOU
BETTER
BE
READY,
JIO!!

DM

ZUP

STOP
IT, JIN!!

SPECIAL
MOVE...

SHA

GWOOO

GWOOO

MAXIMUM
SPIRIT.
INITIATE
O-PART
EFFECT.

O.P.T.: JIN
O-PART: ???
O-PART RANK: B
O-PART EFFECT: FLAME
(+ BLACK FLAME)

I'LL BURN YOUR DREAMS, AND EVERYTHING ELSE, WITH MY BLACK FLAME...

B... BLACK FLAME—

INITIATE O-PART EFFECT!!!

GWOOO

GWOOO

WHAT COULD HIS O-PART EFFECT BE?

I DON'T LIKE HOW THIS FEELS...

DREAMS ARE DREAMS BECAUSE THEY DON'T COME TRUE...

RELEASE SPIRIT!!!

FOR GOD'S SAKE, SABAKI JUST KEEPS ON HIRING O.P.T. AFTER O.P.T.

BUT— IT FEELS DIFFERENT FROM ALL THE SPIRITS I'VE SEEN BEFORE...

TH... THAT'S HIS SPIRIT...

JUST LIKE MY DEAD PARENTS...

...WHO I'LL NEVER BE ABLE TO MEET AGAIN!!

...AREN'T SOMETHING YOU SHOULD TALK ABOUT SERIOUSLY. HA HA HA HA.

HEY, YOU TWO! DREAMS...

ZSH ZSH ZSH ZSH

A KILLER? WHAT DID THIS KID DO?

BUT YOU'VE GOT NO RIGHT TO LAUGH AT AN OLD MAN'S DREAMS!!!

JIN!! YOU'RE FREE TO NOT BELIEVE IN DREAMS IF YOU DON'T WANT TO!!

HUH.

CHAK

AH, I SEE THAT JIO THE CRYBABY HAS GROWN UP.

KID, YOU...

HUH.

JIN!!

THD

THE FACE...

I'VE NEVER FORGOTTEN YOUR FACE.

SO, YOU REMEMBERED AT LAST.

TP

ZSH

UH...

...OF THE ONE WHO KILLED MY PARENTS.

I'LL CRUSH 'EM BOTH!!

H... HOW COULD I MISTAKE HIM?

DAMN IT!! HE SMASHED THAT ENGRAVING FROM THE RUIN...

WE'RE FRIENDS.

JIN.

DON'T WORRY, JIO.

I WAS ORDERED BY A GUY NAMED SABAKI TO KILL THE OLD MAN.

SABAKI...

FWIP FWIP

GSH

YOU AND THAT THAT STUPID DREAM OF YOURS...

TP

CHAPTER 3: THE DREAM 2

O-Parts Hunter

By Seishi Kishimoto

VOL 1

vizmedia

O-Parts HunteR 1

story and art by **SEISHI KISHIMOTO**

Jio is a young boy with a tragic past who only trusts one thing in the world: money. Little does he suspect that he is also a very powerful O.P.T., and inside him sleeps a demon of incredible ferocity. He meets up with a girl named Ruby, and together they decide to embark on a dangerous quest to discover as many O-Parts as they can. Will Jio help Ruby realize her dream of becoming a world famous treasure hunter? More importantly, will Ruby help Jio realize his dream—of *world domination*?!

- $9.99
- **Volumes 1 and 2 available now**

RATED
T+
FOR OLDER TEEN

I LOVE YOU.

...WILL YOU TELL ME WHAT YOU THINK?

YES...

OH...

WHEN YOU'VE READ IT...

GRP

WHO ON EARTH *ARE* YOU?

...BUT IN REALITY, WE PROTECT BOOKS AND ALL THOSE WHO LOVE THEM.

TO THE PUBLIC, WE'RE DETECTIVES...

WE'RE THREE LOVELY SISTERS WHO CONTROL PAPER. WE'RE THE PAPER SISTERS!!

"LOVELY"?

WHAT-EVER.

BANG

WHEW.

NICE ONE!

THERE. OUR JOB'S DONE.

YOU HAVE THE RIGHT TO REMAIN SILENT. YOU HAVE THE RIGHT TO A LAWYER.

BUT...

...YOU HAVE NO RIGHT TO READ ANY BOOKS.

WAM

GH

PTUP

AHH

YOU DID IT, MAGS!

URRK

HOW LONG ARE YOU GONNA KEEP ME WAITING? IT'S JUST ONE BOOK!

EEK

WAP

YEAH?

THAT SO?

krik...

YOU MIGHT GET A GOOD PRICE ON THIS.

ER...IT'S AN UNUSUAL BOOK, SO I'M CHECKING THE CATALOGS.

I'M NOT HIS GIRLFRIEND.

ANYWAY, HE LOVES BOOKS, NOT ME.

WHAT KIND OF CREEP WORRIES MORE ABOUT A BOOK THAN HIS *GIRLFRIEND*?

BUT YOU LIKE *HIM*, HUH?

BIP BIP

!!

HMM

MR. TSAI IS STALLING HIM. HURRY OVER! WE'LL HEAD THERE, TOO!

ROGER!

SOMEONE'S TRYING TO SELL A SUSPICIOUS BOOK AT HONHONDO BOOKSTORE.

WHAT?

LISTEN, THAT BOOK...

I TOLD MY FRIEND, BUT...

I REPORTED IT TO THE POLICE, BUT WHEN I EXPLAINED THAT IT WAS JUST A BOOK, THEY WOULDN'T TAKE ME SERIOUSLY.

...GOT UPSET AND HUNG UP ON ME.

HE JUST...

IT WAS PROBABLY PRECIOUS TO HIM. I CAN'T FIND IT IN ANY BOOKSTORE. HE LOVES BOOKS...

I REMEMBER ONLY RAIN.

MAYBE IT WAS A RARE BOOK. WHAT WAS THE TITLE?

WHAT'S WITH HIM?

HIS GIRLFRIEND WAS *MUGGED!* WHAT A WORM!

IGNORE HER. SHE'S IN A REBELLIOUS STAGE.

AH.

DON'T MAKE EXCUSES FOR ME!

...BUT I *HATE* BOOKS!!

MY SISTERS DON'T FEEL THIS WAY...

NOW, THEN...

...WHAT IS IT YOU WANT?

I BORROWED A BOOK FROM A FRIEND...

...BUT ON MY WAY HOME, THE BAG IT WAS IN...

HER MOTTO IS, "BIG! STRONG! SHARP!"

THAT'S MAGGIE, OUR MIDDLE SISTER.

AND TO PROVE IT...

TUP

FLUTTER

WE'RE BOOK SPECIALISTS. WE'LL ANSWER ANY NEED YOU MIGHT HAVE.

HANG ON!

WHEN SHE'S LOST IN A BOOK, NOT EVEN A NUCLEAR BOMB CAN FAZE HER.

COO COO

SEE?

YOU THINK WE'RE GOING TO GET A **NUCLEAR BOMB?**

HERE AT PAPER SISTERS DETECTIVE COMPANY...

...WE DEAL IN ALL CASES INVOLVING BOOKS.

SEARCHES, RESTORATIONS, TRANSLATIONS, NEGOTIATIONS, APPRAISALS...

BUT WE DON'T GET MUCH WORK.

I HATE MY MOTTO.

OH, ANITA'S STURDY. HER MOTTO IS, "NOT EVEN AN ELEPHANT CAN SQUASH HER!"

HMPH

IT'S TRUE! WE'VE BEEN REDUCED TO TRACKING DOWN LOST PETS!

CHECK OUT MY SCARS!

ANITA! THAT'S A TRADE SECRET!

AN ELEPHANT?

YIKES...

HI! I'M
MICHELLE!

I'M
KELLY!

S-SO
MANY
BOOKS
...

CHAPTER 1

R.O.D: Read or Dream

Story by Hideyuki Kurata
Art by Ran Ayanaga

VOL 1

Three Sisters— One Power

Michelle is a romantic daydreamer and hardcore book collector. Maggie is a soft-spoken bookworm who always gets mistaken for a boy. Anita is a tomboy who doesn't have time for reading. Together, they're the Paper Sisters, three very different siblings united by a strange power—the ability to control paper in any way they desire! And from their Hong Kong detective agency, they solve any and all cases involving books!

- $9.99
- The eagerly awaited follow-up to the hit series *Read or Die*!
- Volumes 1 - 3 available now
- By Hideyuki Kurata, screenwriter of the *Excel Saga* anime

RATED **T+** FOR OLDER TEEN

THUMP THUMP THUMP THUMP THUMP THUMP

I WAS DETERMINED TO TAKE YOU WITH ME (AS A HOSTAGE).

...ON YOU...

FROM THE MOMENT I LAID EYES...

I'M BETTING MY LIFE ON THIS...

THE EYES OF A CRIMINAL

TRUE FEELINGS WILL BE CONVEYED.

THUMP THUMP THUMP THUMP

...

THUMP THUMP THUMP THUMP

DEFINITELY NO CHEATING ALLOWED!!

B-BUT IN RETURN—!!

BUT!!

WHETHER THEY HAVE BEEN CONVEYED ACCURATELY IS ANOTHER MATTER!!

PSSSSH

ALL...

ALL RIGHT...

VWOOSH—

WELL, HOW ABOUT GIVING ME YOUR HOME PHONE NUMBER?

NOW, FOR YOUR CELL... OH, I GUESS YOU DON'T HAVE IT.

O... OKAY...

CHEATING? WHAT'S SHE TALKING ABOUT?

EH?

AH... RIGHT... I KNOW.

...WANT YOU (AS A HOSTAGE).

I...

...TO BECOME ENTANGLED IN A COMPLICATED RELATIONSHIP.

BLUSH

SPARKLE

LATER, THIS DELICATE EXPRESSION CAUSES BOTH OF THEM...

CLOSE

I WOULDN'T JOKE ABOUT...

...SOMETHING LIKE THIS...

OF COURSE I DO!! BUT I'M *SERIOUS* ABOUT THIS!!

DO YOU EVEN REALIZE WHAT YOU'RE SAYING?

JUST BECAUSE CHRISTMAS EVE IS FOR LOVERS, YOU CAN'T JUST BLURT IT OUT LIKE THAT...

F-FOOL!!

WITHIN BREATHING DISTANCE.

WHA

B... BUT!

... I LIKE IT. ♥ BUT, IT'S *WARM.*

BLUSH

ANY-THING? JUST NAME IT! ♥ YEP, *ANYTHING.*

WOOSH

APPRECIA-TION? I'D LIKE TO SHOW MY APPRECIA-TION. I FEEL BAD THAT YOU'RE HELPING ME SO MUCH...

TURN

HUH? WILL YOU... GO WITH ME?

WELL, THEN... I'LL GET STRAIGHT TO THE POINT... OKAY! ♥

IN RETURN FOR SAVING HER, I'LL ASK HER TO BE A HOSTAGE FOR RANSOM. HEH, HEH, HEH... THIS MAKES THINGS EASIER.

THU THUMP THUMP

FWUMP

!

...

AH-CHOO!!

...TO BECOME A MASTER CRIMINAL!!

NAIVE!! YOU'RE SO NAIVE, HAYATE!! THIS IS NO WAY...

YOU'D BETTER WEAR IT.

GIRLS SHOULDN'T LET THEMSELVES GET COLD LIKE THAT...

BUT...

NEVER MIND HOW *BAGGY* IT IS.

IT'S CRUDELY STITCHED, AND THE FABRIC IS HEAVY.

STAB

TREMBLE

WHAT A CHEAP COAT.

BUT YOU SAVED ME...

I'M NOT SURE WHAT HAPPENED...

...

AH... A LITTLE BIT...

EH?

YOU LOOK COLD...

?

WHY AM I BEING THANKED?

ACK. NOT GOOD.

HYU

THIS IS NOT THE TIME TO SHOW HER ANY KINDNESS...

I'M ABOUT TO KIDNAP THIS GIRL AND RECEIVE A HUGE RANSOM!!

WELL, SORRY!! MY HEART IS ALREADY AS COLD AS ICE...

HA!! SO WHAT?! IS THAT ALL? ARE YOU TRYING TO WIN MY SYMPATHY?!

THAT'S WHY I FORGOT MY COAT...

A LOT OF THINGS HAPPENED AT THIS PARTY, SO I RAN AWAY.

SHIVER

... THE HONEST AND EARNEST ...

...ARE THE ONES WHO DESERVE THE LAST LAUGH...

BUT BELIEVE *THIS* ...

HO HO HO

WRONG!!

WHACK

SO THERE'S NO NEED TO HESITATE!!

EVEN IF I'M ARRESTED, AT LEAST I'LL HAVE HOT MEALS AND A BED IN JAIL...

EVEN THAT POOR KID NELLO IN *A DOG OF FLANDERS* DIED BECAUSE HE TRIED TO REMAIN A GOOD PERSON DESPITE ADVERSITY!!

BWAAAHA

BWAAHA

HEH HEH

*IN THE ORIGINAL STORY, AN ANGEL CAME FOR THEM.

...WON'T GET ME ANY-WHERE!!

EARNEST AND HONEST WORK...

IN THIS WORLD, ONLY THE *CUNNING* CAN WIN!!

CHKCHK

HIS DOG PATRASCHE'S LESSON WAS PROBABLY... "IF YOU DON'T WANT TO DIE, THEN BECOME A DEVIL!!"

THAT'S RIGHT, HAYATE!! GO FOR IT!!

THIS MUST BE... A REVELATION FROM NELLO, TELLING ME TO AVENGE HIM!!

AS LUCK WOULD HAVE IT, HERE'S AN EASY CATCH—A GIRL BY HERSELF IN THE PARK AT NIGHT!!

THIS BRINGS US BACK TO THE OPENING SCENE.

KEEP OFF THE GRASS!

WHAT KIND OF PARENTS ARE THEY?

SERIOUSLY... FOR THEM TO GO THIS FAR...

I MANAGED TO ESCAPE...

HE HAS A TALENT HE DOESN'T WANT AWAKENED, IF AT ALL POSSIBLE.

...

FROM MANY YEARS OF EXPERIENCE, THIS BOY CAN TELL WHAT CATEGORY OF YAKUZA THE COLLECTOR BELONGS TO...

ON TOP OF THAT, IT'S 150 MILLION* YEN...

THEY WON'T GIVE UP ON *THAT*, NO MATTER WHAT!!

ONCE THEY DECIDE TO DO IT, THAT KIND OF YAKUZA *WILL* COLLECT, EVEN FROM THE POLICE...

HAAH

HAAH

* Roughly 1.3 million dollars

BUT IF I SLEEP OUTSIDE IN THIS COLD WEATHER, I'LL FREEZE TO DEATH...

I HAVE NO RELATIVES I CAN DEPEND ON, AND I CAN'T TROUBLE MY FRIENDS...

...MEANS COMMITTING A ROBBERY, OR KID-NAPPING SOMEONE FOR RANSOM...

FOR SOMEONE LIKE ME...

...TO COME UP WITH 150 MILLION FAST...

HAAH

HAAH

WHETHER IT'S ROBBERY, OR KID-NAPPING...

...IT'S TO SAVE MY OWN LIFE!!

SOME WRONGDOING SHOULD BE FORGIVEN!! NO, IT *MUST* BE FORGIVEN!!

SINCE IT'S COME DOWN TO THIS, SHOULDN'T I JUST BECOME A BAD GUY?! MY PARENTS, AS WELL AS THE YAKUZA, ARE TARGETING ME...

...I COULDN'T GRASP THE MEANING OF WHAT WAS WRITTEN THERE...

?

FWP

FOR A WHILE...

...A COPY OF AN I.O.U.

...A LETTER ADDRESSED TO ME AND...

INSIDE WAS...

ONES, TENS, HUNDREDS, THOUSANDS... HUNDRED MILLION... ONE HUNDRED AND FIFTY MILLION?

LOAN AGREEMENT

LENDER (FIRST PARTY) GAKKANGUMI
BORROWER (SECOND PARTY) SHUN AYASAKI

TOTAL AMOUNT: 156,804,000

WE'LL LEAVE THE ♥ REST TO YOU ♥

LOANED OUT 156,804,00 YEN

BORROWED. PAPA ♥ MAMA ♥ PLEASE THANKS ♥

...WHAT'S THIS? AN I.O.U.?

HUH?

"DO YOUR BEST TO PAY IT BACK"?!

SANTA HAD LEFT ME A *DEBT*.

EH? WHAT? IT CAN'T BE?!

"WE'LL LEAVE THE REST TO YOU"?!

RUSTLE

... YOU'RE FIRED. AYASAKI-KUN.

I HEARD THAT YOU'RE ONLY 16 YEARS OLD.

OUR HIRING POLICY IS 18 YEARS AND OLDER...

AYASAKI-KUN, YOU LIED ABOUT YOUR AGE.

YOU'RE DEFINITELY THE BEST AND FASTEST IN OUR COMPANY.

I'VE BEEN DOING MY SHARE OF WORK...

W... WHY IS THAT?!

THEN WHY ?!

YOUR PARENTS WERE HERE EARLIER AND TOLD ME ABOUT IT.

H-HOW ...

...DID YOU ...?!

YOU GAVE IT TO *THEM*? ALL OF MY PAY WENT TO *MY PARENTS* ?!!

HUH ?!

ANYWAY, I GAVE THE 170,000 YEN FOR A MONTH'S PAY TO YOUR PARENTS.

HERE I THOUGHT YOU WERE AN EARNEST, EXCEPTIONAL YOUNG MAN, BUT YOU'VE BETRAYED ME.

REALLY ...

Why did my parents ...?

EH?!

IF THEIR UNEMPLOYMENT WAS DUE TO LAY-OFFS RESULTING FROM CORPORATE RESTRUCTURING RESULTING FROM AN ECONOMIC DOWNTURN, OR EVEN AN ACCIDENT...

...

YOU TOO, GIVE IT YOUR BEST...

Y... YEAH...

HAVE FUN AT THE PARTY!

WELL...

GLOOM...

SHUFFLE

SHUFFLE

KCHAK

...THERE WOULD BE ROOM FOR SYMPATHY.

I'M BUYING DREAMS. ♥

MOMMY'S NOT BUYING HORSE-RACING TICKETS.

AND MY MOM...

...SAYS THAT, AND NEGLECTS THE HOUSEKEEPING.

MOM

...WORK MORE SUITABLE AND MEANINGFUL FOR ME.

I THINK THERE MUST BE...

BUT MY DAD...

...DREAMS ON AND DOESN'T LOOK FOR A STEADY JOB.

DAD

...THE HONEST AND EARNEST ARE THE ONES WHO DESERVE THE LAST LAUGH...

WHOOSH

BUT I BELIEVE...

THOSE WHO DON'T WORK... DON'T EAT!!

MONEY'S MORE IMPORTANT THAN FRIENDSHIP, EH?

OH... AS USUAL, YOU WON'T HANG OUT WITH US...

YEAH...

PART-TIME JOB, MEANING BIKE MESSENGER?

BUT I DON'T HAVE ANY MONEY, AND I'M STILL ON MY PART-TIME JOB...

UHHH...

...

BUT IF I JOIN A CLUB...

I'LL HAVE LESS TIME FOR MY PART-TIME JOB...

SO WHY DON'T YOU JOIN THE SOCCER CLUB OR SOMETHING, INSTEAD OF JUST WORKING AT YOUR PART-TIME JOB?

HAYATE-KUN, YOU'RE ATHLETIC...

WHY DO YOU NEED MONEY SO BADLY, ANYWAY?!

YEAH, YEAH, YOU WANT MONEY THAT MUCH?!

YEESH!! *JOB* THIS, *JOB* THAT, YOU SOME KIND OF MONEY-GRUBBER?!

NO... DON'T WORRY ABOUT IT...

S-SORRY...

WE GOT CARRIED AWAY...

...

...ARE UNEMPLOYED...

UH... MY PARENTS...

...I'M AN AVERAGE 10TH GRADER AT AN ORDINARY PUBLIC HIGH SCHOOL.

TO THINK, THIS IS CHRISTMAS EVE...

ALTHOUGH I WORK AS A BICYCLE DELIVERY BOY...

MY NAME IS HAYATE AYASAKI.

OWWW...

GEEZ...

HEH

SKITCH SKITCH

WHAT'S WRONG WITH "ORDINARY"?

What's with the explanation?

BTW, I'm in 10th grade

AH... WELL, WELL, IF IT ISN'T SOME OF MY CLASSMATES, WHO ATTEND THAT ORDINARY PUBLIC HIGH SCHOOL.

!!

HEYYY!! HAYATE!!

I'VE GOT MY REASONS TO BE WORKING ON CHRISTMAS EVE...

IT'S ALL YOU CAN EAT AND DRINK, JUST 3,000 YEN.

HAYATE-KUN, WOULD YOU LIKE TO COME, TOO?!

OH, YEAH!!

AH!! DON'T TELL ME, A CHRISTMAS PARTY?!

WHAT'S UP? A GET-TOGETHER?

BAM RATTLE CRASH

TINK

HE ACTUALLY STOOD UP!!

OHH!! HE STOOD UP!!

OHH!

TP

...

...

...

SHHH HHH

SIGN THIS SLIP, PLEASE.

I'M BICYCLE DELIVERY MESSENGER, HAYATE AYASAKI.

FWIP

RUMORS TO THE CONTRARY, SANTA WAS BRUTALLY HONEST.

WELL, BECAUSE... YOUR FAMILY IS *POOR*.

YOU WANT TO KNOW WHY?

WHY DIDN'T YOU BRING ME ANY PRESENTS?

HEY, SANTA-SAN...

I ASKED SANTA IN A DREAM, LONG AGO.

SHOCK

BUT BELIEVE THIS...

GET WHAT YOU WANT WITH YOUR OWN TWO HANDS.

"THOSE WHO DON'T WORK, DON'T EAT."

SPARKLE

WORK, BOY!!

B-BUT, WHAT AM I GONNA DO?! I WANT A GAME BOY!!

EH?!

Panic Panic

AT LEAST, NOT TO YOUR PLACE ...!!

I WON'T BE COMING BACK HERE AGAIN, EVER...!!

THOSE FINAL WORDS WORRIED ME, BUT...

FLOAT

FLOAT

I DECIDED THEN TO BELIEVE THOSE WORDS, AND LIVE ON.

EH?! WHAT?! WHAT DO YOU MEAN?!

HEY... WAIT...

Panic Panic

THE HONEST AND EARNEST ARE THE ONES WHO DESERVE THE LAST LAUGH...

BUT EVEN THEN, I WON'T BE GIVING YOU A PRESENT.

Episode 1:
"Santa's Red Is a Blood-Colored Hell"

Hayate the Combat Butler

By Kenjiro Hata

Hardworking Hayate has a plan to pay back the yakuza—who are now the legal owners of his vital organs: he'll kidnap someone and ransom them for a mountain of money. But things get tricky when his would-be kidnap-pee—who as luck would have it is the daughter of a mind-bogglingly wealthy family—mistakes Hayate's actions for a confession of love, and hires him to be her personal servant. At least his employment future is secure, or so he thinks...

- $9.99
- Volumes 1 and 2 available now
- Released quarterly

RATED
T+
FOR OLDER TEEN

More About the True-Life Pop Culture Hit *Train_Man*!

Who is Hidenori Hara?

Hidenori Hara is a 20-year veteran manga artist who specializes in the coming-of-age romance genre. Previous works include *Fuyu Monogatari* (Winter Tale), *Someday*, and *Regatta*. Hara's work has been serialized in *Shonen Sunday*, *Big Comics Spirits*, and *Young Sunday*. His most recent project is *Hoshi no Furu Machi: When You Wish Upon a Star.*

Who is Hitori Nakano?

Densha Otoko was based on an online thread on 2Channel, Japan's largest Internet bulletin board site. The fictitious name, Hitori Nakano, was selected as the author's name when this story was published in book format. When read in the Japanese order, with surname followed by given name, Nakano Hitori is a homonym for a phrase that means "one among many"—representing all the single men who gathered on the online discussion forum that hosted this thread.

What is Akihabara?

Akihabara is Tokyo's shopping mecca for electronics and software. Akihabara, or Akiba for short, has also become famous for being a center of otaku culture with throngs of stores selling anime, video games and other ancillary merchandise.

What is on the background of the cover?

"キタ━━━(ﾟ∀ﾟ)━━━!!!" is used in the background of the front and back covers and would be transliterated as "Kita ━━━(ﾟ∀ﾟ)━━━!!!! "
"Kita" literally means "(it) came." Sometimes it's used literally, such as when finally receiving a long-awaited e-mail or phone call, but it is also used in the sense of being emotionally moved, or even as a reaction to something like strong wasabi. It has been localized in this series as "w00t." The other symbols on the cover are all examples of Japanese emoticons. For example "(ﾟ∀ﾟ)" represents an excited face. Japanese emoticons have been retained throughout this manga. A few other examples of note include the following:

(;ﾟ∀ﾟ)=3   An excited face with sweat or tears running down.
            The "=3" represents a puff of air to accompany the panting.

_| ̄|○   A man down on his hands and knees in shame.

\(ﾟДﾟ)/   Excited face with open mouth and hands waving in the air.

What is "drftgyhujikolp;["?

"drftgyhujikolp;[" can represent extreme exasperation, surprise, or anything else that cannot be expressed in words. It's formed by taking a couple fingers and dragging them across a standard QWERTY keyboard.

I WAS VERY MOVED BY YOUR COURAGE.

I'M THE ONE WHO WAS SITTING NEXT TO YOU ON THE TRAIN.

I WAS VERY MOVED ...

MOVED ...

SNIFF

SNIFF

w00t ————(°∀°)———— !!!!!

CLENCH CLENCH

AHH!

IT'S FROM ONE OF THOSE WOMEN ...

I WONDER ...

AM I SUPPOSED TO WRITE BACK TO HER ...?

NOW THERE'S AN EXPRESS DELIVERY PACKAGE HERE FOR YOU!

HEY!

TWO DAYS LATER ...

I'M HOME ...

A LETTER ...?

OH!

WELCOME BACK ...

THERE'S A LETTER FOR YOU.

TH... THIS IS ...

S-SORRY...

UM...I'M SORRY YOU ALL HAD TO GET INVOLVED IN THIS MESS BECAUSE OF ME...

IT'S HARD TO FIND PEOPLE LIKE YOU NOWADAYS, YOUNG MAN.

OH!

WHAT ARE YOU SAYING?

THAT'S RIGHT...

LET ME TELL YOU!

AH, ISN'T YOUR SON TAKING THE ENTRANCE EXAMS THIS YEAR?

NOW MY SON, HE'S ANOTHER STORY...

YOUR SON IS A FINE YOUNG MAN!

OH, NO!

I WISH MY SON COULD BE MORE LIKE YOU!

So that's what happened…

I was pretty pitiful.

That salaryman was kewl.

The conductor came by a little later.

He wanted to press charges, so the old man, those women, that girl and I all got off at the next station.

We went to the police station to fill out some paperwork.

Come on, say something clever. ⌐□○

OKAY...

THAT'S ENOUGH!

HRGH

YOU BRAT!

DON'T MESS WITH ME!

YEE EE

MISTER, ACT YOUR AGE AND STOP HARASSING THIS YOUNG KID...

HM?

WHAT, YA BASTARD!

DON'T GET IN MY SZGH... BAH!

THANK... YOU

Y... YESS...

AH....

YOU CAN GO BACK TO YOUR SEAT.

I CAN TAKE IT FROM HERE.

GAAAAAAH!!

DID YOU JUST TELL ME TO "STOP IT"!?

WHAT'RE YOU STARING AT!?

T... T-T-T... TWENTY-TWO...!

HUH!? HOW OLD ARE YOU?

OH NOOOOO!!

GO AHEAD, CALL THE POLICE OR MZZLE FLZGT... AGH!

YOU ROTTEN BRAT... I'M OVER SIXTY WRFLX...YA WANNA DO THIS!?

I'M CALLING THE POLICE!

D... DO WHAT?

w00t ━━━━━━━━ (ﾟ∀ﾟ) ━━━━━ !!!!!

episode 1:
Birth of the Train_Man

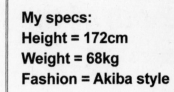

My specs:
Height = 172cm
Weight = 68kg
Fashion = Akiba style

I'm a gamer/anime otaku,
your typical Akihabara type.

Age = Years without a girlfriend.

Of course, I'm a V.

episode 1:
Birth of the Train_Man

Went to Akiba today. Didn't go to buy anything specific.

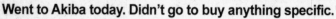

I normally just lurk, so I don't know how well I can write about what happened. Try not to laugh.